Texas Pete
IN RED PEPPER

By RICHARD & PHILIP HARPER

Illustrated by MARILYN STEVENS

WWW.MARILYNSTEVENSART.COM

Ministries

Texas Pete in Red Pepper

Harper Brothers Printing Ministries
111 North Vandala Court
King, NC 27021

©2011 Richard and Philip Harper Publishers
ISBN: 978-60208-276-2
First Printing June 2011
Second Printing July 2011
Third Printing August 2011
Fourth Printing September 2012
Fifth Printing February 2013
Sixth Printing January 2014

Cover Design-Glenn Stevenson

Illustrated by-Marilyn Stevens
www.marilynstevensart.com

All images used by permission

Printed in Canada by
Bethel Baptist Church
4212 Campbell Street
North London, ON N6P 1A6
www.bethelbaptist.ca

Dedication

This book is dedicated to our father, Howard Harper. From the beginning of our lives he taught us the importance of dedication and hard work. We would like to take this opportunity to thank him for being "Dad" and to thank the Lord for him.

Table of Contents

Chapter 1

Texas Pete and the Gang

If you came out to visit me in the Old West you might be lucky to see a few things that you couldn't see anyplace else. You may see a gunfighter brave enough to stare down his opponent in the middle of the town square at high noon, you could see one man with enough courage to fight six other men outside of the saloon, you may even get to meet some people brave enough to leave their comfortable homes back East for the chance to stake their claim and wade out into the middle of a river to pan for gold. Yes, the Old West was filled with all kinds of rootin' tootin' cowboys showing all kinds of bravery. But there was one thing that you almost never saw, and that was an *hombre* with enough gumption to head out to the frontier and start a church. See, folks around these parts don't take kindly to that sort of thing. At least that was the case out here in Red Pepper, Texas. Through the years several parsons (that is what they called preachers back then) headed out to Red Pepper and they all had the same goal in mind; to turn our rough and tumble town into a place filled with sweet, little, lily-livered, church goin' folk, and like I said, folks just didn't take kindly to that sort of thing.

One thing seems to be true no matter where you go; people by nature are all sinners. That was the case here in Red Pepper. But there was a gang of fellows here that seemed to be a little bit worse than most folks. Matter of fact, most of the town folk were afraid of them. They were the reason for most of the violence and crime in Red Pepper. They were known in the West by several names, but here in town, folks mostly called them the *Chili Pepper Gang*. They had no regard for human life; they disobeyed every law that was passed, and they lived their lives quickly and violently. They seemed to hate everybody, but most of all, they hated preachers. I think most of the troubles with the *Chili Pepper Gang* stemmed from their leader, an ornery fellow by the name of Texas Pete. The local sheriff described him as huge, mean, ornery, nasty, evil, dangerous, and scary, and those were his good traits.

Usually as stories are told and retold they seem to get bigger with each telling, but with Texas Pete, the stories never quite did him justice. He was actually meaner than his legend. I guess you could sum it up by saying that Texas Pete and his gang were about as bad a bunch of criminals the west had ever seen.

One of the stories told about ole' Pete was about him and Parson Fred who came out here to start a church. Parson Fred was walking down town one evening when he saw Texas Pete standing outside the saloon. The parson walked over, and, nice as he could be, tried to hand Pete a flyer, telling him about the new church he was starting. As he handed him the flyer the parson asked Pete, "Sir, if you were to die tonight, where would you spend eternity?" Ole' Pete didn't know anything about Heaven or Hell, and I don't think he even knew what "eternity" was. But he knew this little parson man asked him about dying, and he took it as a threat! He reached out with one hand and grabbed the parson by the collar while his other hand formed a giant fist. He was just about to turn Parson Fred's lights out, when he heard a high pitched little scream come from the man. "Wait! Please don't hurt me," Fred said in a voice higher and louder than any soprano that ever sang in a church choir.

Texas Pete realized that this little man was no threat at all; so he let go of his collar and, in his most imposing voice, asked the parson, "Are you trying to start trouble Mister?"

Fred answered him with a quivering stutter, "NNNNo, sssir, IIIII. Wwwaaanttt to..."

"Well stop stalling and speak up now!!" barked Pete.

"Start a church and..."

He was cut off right away with a sharp response

from Pete. "We do not want a church, we do not need a church, and I will personally see to it that there will never be a church here in Red Pepper, Texas. If I ever hear another word out of your mouth there's gonna be trouble!!!" With that, Pete threw Parson Fred to the ground, and the entire *Chili Pepper Gang* gathered

around to mock and laugh at poor Fred.

Most of the town folk kinda liked old Fred, but no one wanted to stand up to Pete or his gang! From that time on Parson Fred just stopped talking. Some folks believed he chose not to talk, but others believed old Pete just "scared the talk right out of him."

Chapter 2

Parson Bill

About two years had passed since the famed Parson Fred event, and the town of Red Pepper just kept getting worse and worse. Although Parson Fred was not able to speak, he was still able to pray silently (God hears us when we pray whether out loud or silently), and every night he would ask God to revive that little town somehow. Even in his fear of Texas Pete, Parson Fred always held out hope that one day his little church would take root and start to grow. But now, after two years of no change, even Fred was starting to have his doubts. Even though Fred didn't know it, God was already answering his prayer.

In the southern part of Texas there was another preacher that God was preparing to come to Red Pepper, someone a little younger, and a little tougher than Fred had been when he showed up. This young fellow was just called, "Parson Bill." He wasn't any bigger than Fred, in fact he was a little shorter, but he had so much faith in the Lord that he kinda *looked bigger!*

Parson Bill had been an outlaw in his youth and

was almost as mean and tough as Texas Pete, but one day he met an old preacher on the streets of Heart Burn Gulch, Texas, who told him something he had never heard. The old preacher just said, "Son, did you know that Jesus loves you?" That little question changed his life forever. It was not often that an outlaw was loved by anyone (except maybe his momma), but when he heard that someone loved him even as bad he was, it just broke his old hard heart. All of a sudden he found himself wanting to hear more from the old preacher. The preacher told him some things he didn't want to hear -like that he was a sinner. Now Bill knew he was a sinner, (but no one likes to hear that) and that there is punishment for sinners; he also told Bill more about this Jesus and how much He loved Bill! Bill was amazed when he heard that Jesus loved him so much that He died...just for Bill!

Before the preacher could really get finished telling him the story, Bill said, "Reverend, I ain't never said this about any man, but I love this Jesus fella too!" As tears ran down the dusty cheeks of this once hardened criminal, he prayed a simple prayer right there, in the middle of the street of Heart Burn, and asked Jesus to save him! From that day forward Bill was a new man! He wanted nothing to do with crime, but now he wanted to learn everything he could about the Bible! Eventually Bill became a parson, and the Lord lead him to Red Pepper, and Parson Bill was just the kind of man Red Pepper, Texas needed.

Early one Friday morning before the sun came up over the Picante Valley that surrounded Red Pepper Texas, the sound of slow moving horse hooves echoed triumphantly as Parson Bill made his way into town. A little sand storm had blown through the valley, and it had covered Bill with dust and had blown the hat off of his head. He was a little disappointed because he wanted to make a good first impression on the town folk. He arrived in town near nine o'clock in the morning, and as he jumped off his horse he began to look around. To his left was a saloon, just beyond that was the local barber shop with a sign out front that said "Hair cuts: two bits, shaves free (at yer own risk)". On his right was yet another saloon "Haught and Spicey's Saloon", named after the two owners Tom Haught, and Carl Spicey. Just two buildings down from Spicey's was the Harbanero National Bank. That bank had been robbed at least fifteen times in the last year (everyone knew it was the *Chili Pepper Gang*, but no one was willing to tell), and right past that was the Sheriff's office and the jail house. The tumbleweeds rolled across Bill's foot as he stared at the town. It was quiet at nine in the morning, but he knew at night this was a very dangerous place. It would have been enough to make most men turn around and run the other way, but Parson Bill took it all in, smiled, and said "Well, Lord, it seems there is a lot of work to be done here, and I cannot do it on my own. You promised that you would never leave me nor forsake me, and without you I can do nothing, so I am asking for help. In Jesus' name, Amen." It was just then, he saw an old man sitting outside the Haught and Spicy Saloon. He was a rough looking character, not because he was mean, but probably because he had lived a hard life on the frontier. He was sitting on the porch of the saloon with his back against the wall. His arms were up in the air and his fingers were laced behind his head. Although he was not asleep his hat was covering his eyes as he relaxed and chewed on his tobacco. He had a spittoon setting just close enough to his chair so that he was able to spit right into the can without even needing to move. Parson Bill walked right up to him and said, "Excuse me sir, could you please tell me where I can find the meanest most orneriest man in this town?"

The old man sat up straight and pulled his hat back further on his head revealing a face that was bronze from sitting in the sun and wrinkled from the difficult life he had lived. He stared up and down Parson Bill and then asked "Who are you stranger, and why do you want to die?" With this he leaned over and spit into the can.

Parson Bill stiffened as he looked deeply into the man's face and answered, "No, I just want to talk to him." The old man tipped his hat just a little more and with a small smirk on his face he said, "And what is so all-fired important that you are aimin' to say to him?"

Bill spoke with a purpose that caught the old timer off guard as he said, "I want to tell him that I am going to start a church in this town and I always like to look my enemies in the eye."

Chapter 3

The Thirty-Sixth Step

"You want to tell him what?" The little old man said as he almost choked on his tobacco.

"You heard me", he replied, "I want to start a church here in Red Pepper, Texas." The old fellow started thinking about the day Texas Pete met Parson Fred. It happened almost exactly where this new preacher man was standing. He couldn't help but chuckle as he pictured Parson Bill begging for his life the same way Fred did! Soon the chuckle turned to a good old fashioned belly laugh. The stranger laughed so hard he almost fell off of his chair. Bill just looked at him and tried to figure out what was so funny.

After a good two minute laugh the old-timer said, "Stranger, you have no idea what yer fixin' to do."

Bill stood up a little straighter; he could almost feel his own backbone stiffen as he set his jaw and said, "Nonetheless, I would still like to know where I can find the orneriest critter in your town; do you even know who that might be?" Maybe it was the deep tone to his voice, maybe it was the look in his eyes, but there was something in Bill that made the old man stop laughing.

This preacher wasn't going to be scared away, and this conversation wasn't ending until the parson got some answers.

"Sure, that would be old Texas Pete; he's the leader of the *Chili Pepper Gang*. If you want mean and ornery then he's yer man."

"Thank you old-timer for the information, now will you point me in the right direction to find this Texas Pete fellow?" The old man didn't know what to say; not only did this preacher want to talk to Pete, but he wanted to go to his house! It was now obvious that there was no arguing with this preacher, he was either going to start a church here or die trying.

The old timer pointed off in the distance, "You see that tall mountain over yonder?" Bill just nodded, he had been over some mountains in his time but he didn't remember ever seeing a mountain so high or paths so steep and rocky. His stare was interrupted by the scrawny fellow's voice, "Well, that thar is Mt. Cayenne and old Pete lives up on the very top of it. If you are so all fired sure that you want to go to Pete's house then head over to the base of the mountain and start up the trail."

"Which trail, I am sure there are several?" asked Bill.

"You won't have any trouble finding it...it's the one with the big signs that say 'keep out'. You follow that trail way up until you are looking down on the clouds and then you will see Pete's steps." The man continued to tell Bill about the steps; how Pete had built forty-five steps up to his front porch and how no one except Pete had ever made it to the top of the steps! When Bill asked why, the now talkative fellow told him about the thirty-sixth step!

It seems that Pete had measured and figured out that the thirty-sixth step was the first one that put a stranger in range of his six shooters. He actually made sure that the thirty-sixth step had a very distinctive squeak to it. As you hit that step, Pete's horse, Tobasco, would hear the annoying sound and let out a special whinny. The next sound, and the last sound you would hear would be the crack of Pete's trusty pistol. "If'n you were to count the steps on the way up," the old timer said, "when you get to thirty-six you would not be able to count no more," the old fellow so delicately put it!

The old man was sure that the mere telling of the story of the thirty-sixth step would send the young preacher heading out of town, to take his wide-eyed church planting idea to some other town, but Parson Bill looked at the old man and thanked him for the information and warning, letting him know that he had not come this far just to quit because of fear. As he started toward his horse, the old man yelled, "Preacher, once you get to that step you had better have you a weapon."

Bill said, "I have a more powerful weapon than any gun, no need to worry about me."

Now this piqued the old man's interest, "May I see that weapon?!"

To the old fellow's amazement, when the parson pulled his hand out of his saddlebag, he didn't have a shotgun, a peacemaker, or even a Colt forty-five. All he had was a very worn out old Bible that at one time was probably jet black, but over the years, through constant use, it had faded. He said: "This is my weapon, and I trust more in it than any old pistol. Why, it tells me that the God I serve is so powerful that He was able to make an entire sea split right down the middle, and I just do not know of any pistol that is a match for that; so I will just keep trusting in Him, and I will not lose."

Parson Bill politely nodded to the elderly

gentleman, climbed on his trusty horse, and then made his way to the foot of Mount Cayenne. When he got to the "keep out" sign he gently stroked his horse and said, "Why don't you stay here this time boy; this is going to be a long hike."

He dismounted his horse and started up that gigantic mountain. Sure enough, when he got about half way up he noticed the very rickety set of stairs the older man had mentioned. He also noticed he needed to be in a little better shape. He started counting as he climbed "one...two...three..." Before he knew it, he had made it to step thirty-three; he stopped for a moment and began to recollect the warning given by the older gentleman outside Haught and Spicey's saloon: "...When you get to thirty-six you would not be able to count no more." Instead of letting this worry him, he got down on his knees and prayed. For thirty minutes he prayed on that thirty-third step, then he got up, and kept climbing and counting "Thirty-four...thirty-five..." When all of a sudden he heard the sound of a gunshot and saw the dust that covered the thirty-sixth stair blow in the wind. He then heard a rough and tough voice coming from the top of the mountain, "One more step and you'll be in my range stranger, now GIT!" Old Texas Pete was used to people tucking tail and running and he was not ready for the answer he got in return. "Fire if you want to Pete, but I will take that next step. I come to you in the name of Jesus Christ; the One who loved you enough to die for you. If you fire that weapon you may miss out on hearing about someone who loves you even when you are being meaner than a rattlesnake for no reason at all!" With his heart pounding, and sweat dripping from his brow, Bill lifted his right foot slowly and at an even slower speed he placed that foot in the very center of that thirty-sixth step when all of a sudden he heard a loud "crack" echo in his ears.

Pete was six foot five inches tall, weighed at least two hundred and fifty pounds and must have worn a size twenty-three boot

Chapter 4

Changes in Red Pepper

The old boards from that rickety staircase cracked as he placed his full weight on that thirty-sixth step! The snapping of the two-by-four made a sound just like a gun shot. The fact that Bill didn't see the dust fly up or feel the sting of a bullet made him realize (much to his joy and amazement!) that Pete did not shoot him. He did not know why he had not been shot, nor did he care, but he decided that standing there would just give Pete a better shot at a stationary target, so he decided to keep moving. He then did something that no man had ever done before. He stepped up on step thirty-seven. As he stepped up on the thirty-seventh step he could now see the front porch of Pete's house and, to his amazement, there was no one there. Bill became emboldened and took the last eight steps two at a time. It was obvious this tough talking, quick drawing, Parson scaring, stage coach robbing, gang leader had let Bill live; now there was just one question Bill needed to have answered..."Why?"

As he slowly approached the run down, dilapidated, old house of Texas Pete, his pace slowed down. He was moving almost in slow motion when he finally got to the opened front door. He gently knocked on the tattered screen door and began to call out "Hellllooo, Mr. Pete. It's me, Parson Bill, I've come to tell you something very important!"

As he inched closer and closer to the house he heard a deep voice call out from the back of the house, "Why don't you just go away?"

Bill was shocked at how deep Pete's voice was! He felt the little hairs on the back of his neck stand up and goose bumps started to rise up on his arms. He wasn't backing down now! "If I go away now, you may never get to hear what I have to tell you. It looks like you don't get many visitors. Now, will you please come out where I can see you?" Bill was not ready for what he was about to see. Out of the back room of the house came the biggest man he had ever seen. Pete was six foot five inches tall, weighed at least two hundred and fifty pounds and must have worn a size twenty-three boot; the shot gun he held looked like a toy in comparison to his large hands. Bill took a big gulp, took off his hat, wiped his sweaty brow with his sleeve, and greeted Pete with his hand extended for a handshake. Pete just stared at his visitor, his hands gripping firmly to the shotgun. Bill said, "Pete, it would be a lot easier to talk to you if you would put that gun down, I mean you no harm."

Pete released the grip he had on his gun and set it in the corner as he sat in an old dusty chair that seemed too small for his large frame. He said, "You'd better make this quick Parson, I have somewhere to be soon." *The Chili Pepper Gang* was all ready to rob the 4:15 stage, and Pete had to leave in ten minutes to meet the gang.

Parson Bill said, "Ok, Pete, let me ask you a question: If you were to die today, do you know where you would spend eternity?" This question was the question that had been echoing in the back of Pete's mind since the day Parson Fred asked him and now he was hearing it again. Pete was as tough as the stories that were told about him and had never been afraid of anything before, but, for the first time in his life, he was scared.

His booming voice was actually shaking with fear when he finally answered the parson: "Yes, I believe I do." Judging by the tone of voice, Parson Bill knew Ole Pete was not happy with his answer.

As his goose bumps began to develop goose bumps of their own, he risked his life further and leaned over to Pete and said, "Would you like to know how to go to heaven when you die?"

Pete's fear turned to shock. "Oh, that could never happen Parson; I've done too many bad things in my time. I don't know how much you know about me, but I've been a pretty mean man my whole life."

Bill smiled and said, "Pete, I have heard a few stories about you. I reckon everyone from Heart Burn Gulch, all the way down to Hotter'n Blue Blazes Valley has heard stories of Texas Pete, and I know you have done some bad things. But you have to know that when Jesus died on the cross, He paid for every sin that had been or ever would be committed. He paid the full price for every one of your sins! Pete, all you have to do to be forgiven for your sins is recognize you need to be forgiven, believe Jesus died for your sins, and then simply ask Jesus to save you from the judgment to come."

Now to Pete, this sounded a little too easy. He looked at Parson Bill and said, "I've heard about Jesus before. When I was a little tyke, my momma used to take me to Sunday school, and we heard all about Jesus. He may be able to save little boys and girls, but even He can't save someone as bad as me!"

Bill had just the right answer, "Jesus is able to save even the worst of people in this world. As a matter of fact I haven't always been a parson. A few years back I was an outlaw almost as bad as you, but one day a man told me that Jesus loved me and wanted to save me. I decided that I was not going to pass up on something as wonderful as salvation! I figured that if He wanted to

save me then I wanted to be saved! If He still loved me as ornery as I was then I wanted to serve Him! However, this is not about me today, Pete; it is about you. What are you going to do?"

There was a long pause...silence so thick you could cut it with a knife. Bill was beginning to think that Pete was never going to answer when suddenly Pete jumped to his feet with tears streaming down his cheeks and boomed, "Parson, I need to be saved!" It was there, on top of Mount Cayenne that Parson Bill experienced the blessing of leading a giant to Christ and a criminal became a Christian!

Chapter 5

Pete's Prayer

As Pete stood up he couldn't help but know that he was a new man! He had never put much stock in "feelings" and "emotion," but he sure did feel better, and he had never been this emotional. Inside he was as happy as he had ever been, and yet he couldn't stop his eyes from watering. Parson Bill stayed on his knees for an extra moment or two and thanked the Lord for what He had just done in Pete's heart. As the preacher began to stand he felt like he was trapped in a vise as two big arms wrapped around him. Parson Bill began to struggle to breathe as Pete squeezed him in the tightest bear hug he had ever felt. With one giant lift Pete picked Bill up off of the ground like he was nothing! When Texas Pete gave a hug he held nothing back. Finally Pete set the preacher down on the ground and turned him loose. It was then that old Pete took off his ten gallon hat and began waving it above his head as he let out a giant "YeeeeeHaaaaw" that echoed all through the Cayenne Valley! It sure did feel good to be saved.

After several minutes of whooping and hollering

Pete calmed down and looked at Bill and asked a simple question... "Now what, Preacher?"

Parson Bill reached into his bag and pulled out a brand new jet black, leather bound Bible, handed it to

Pete and said, "Well, you have to start by reading this. The Bible is what the Lord uses to speak to us."

"Well Preacher, I really want to read that purty new Bible you have there, but I was wondering...is there a verse in there about robbing a stage coach?" Bill had been asked a lot of questions in his life, but this one took him by surprise.

He thought for a moment and said "Well, there's nothing in here specifically about stage coach robbing, but one of the Ten Commandments says 'Thou shalt not steal.' Why do you ask?"

Pete swallowed hard and then answered, "I was supposed to meet the *Chili Pepper Gang* in a half hour and we were gonna rob the 4:15 stage coach out of Scalded Tongue, Texas, but I don't think I'm gonna go now. They'll just have to rob that coach without me!" Parson Bill spoke up immediately and told Pete that it was a good idea that he not rob the coach but then reminded him that there would be innocent people that could get hurt if his old gang continued with their robbery. A look of shock came over Pete's face, and he yelled excitedly, "Someone needs to stop them!!" With that he darted out of the house faster than greased lightning and jumped on Tobasco, and began down the hill so fast that

33

all you could see was a large cloud of prairie dust where Pete used to be.

As Pete and Tobasco thundered through the valley that surrounded Red Pepper Texas they stirred up a cloud so big that the town folk thought there was a dust storm coming! Pete wasn't really concentrating on the riding. He was too busy thinking about stopping his old gang from robbing that coach. How was he gonna explain to them that it was wrong to steal, and what were they going to say when he told them that the Bible actually had a commandment about it. After all, the *Chili Pepper Gang* wasn't known for their Bible reading. It was beginning to look like Pete was going to get there in the nick of time when all of a sudden Tobasco reared straight up in the air, let out a frightened neigh, and threw Texas Pete right out of the saddle. Pete was so busy concentrating on what he was going to say to the *Chili Pepper Gang* that he didn't have time to brace himself for the fall that was coming. He fell off Tobasco and landed right on his head. The force of the fall left Pete unconscious. The last thing Pete remembered seeing before he went out cold was Tobasco riding away from the valley as fast as he could. Pete woke up moments

later lying flat on his back; his head felt like it was going to split in half. He was also aware that a very large bump was forming on his head, and as he rubbed it, he laughed to himself. He pictured his hat sitting on top of the bump instead of on his head. He laid on the ground laughing to himself and decided to stay there for a minute while his head cleared, but as he lay there, he kept hearing a very faint, familiar sound. He knew he had heard the sound before but, with his head still in a fog, he just wasn't able to place it. He decided he was just going to ignore it and get up. He started to reach to his right and grab his hat when it finally dawned on him what that sound was. He lost his breath for a minute as he realized he was smack dab in the middle of Rattlesnake Canyon. He was surrounded by poisonous, slithering rattlesnakes as far as the eye could see. At least he knew what scared old Tobasco. As he lay on the ground alone, surrounded by dozens of rattlers, his trusty horse gone, and his saddle bag with his pistol gone with him, he began to do something he had never done before; he began to pray, loudly. "Lord, I know that I just met You just a little while ago, but the preacher said I am one of Your children now, and I sure do need Your help. I'm in a pretty big mess here! You see I am surrounded by snakes and I cannot figure out a way to get out of here. Now Parson Bill told me that You are powerful enough to save an old outlaw like me forever, so, I know You can deliver me from a few snakes. In Jesus' name, Amen." He finished his prayer and laid there helplessly watching the rattlers get closer and closer.

Chapter 6

The Chili Pepper Gang

No sooner had ole Pete finished his prayer, and just when he thought things couldn't get any worse; he heard the crack of a gun shot! Now why would anyone waste a bullet on Texas Pete when those rattlesnakes were going to finish him off in just a minute anyway? Pete jumped at the sound, but he noticed the gun shot had scared the snakes as well. Soon another shot rang out, then another, and another, each one hitting close to Pete but all missing him. Just when Pete was sure the shooter was just a terrible shot he saw a rope land on the canyon floor right beside him! Whoever was doing the shooting wasn't shooting at Pete, he was scaring the snakes away so he could rescue Pete! Just then, Pete heard a voice yell, "Grab the rope, and I'll pull you out!" Pete knew he had heard the voice before but he couldn't place it. Pete reached over and grabbed the rope, and immediately he was pulled up the canyon wall and away from the snakes! With each pull on the rope the strange voice offered encouragement. "I've gotcha!" "Hang on Partner" or "It won't be long now!" It was driving Pete crazy trying to place the voice. When he finally reached the top he wanted to see the face of the stranger that had saved him, but he had pulled so hard on the last tug of the rope that all Pete could see was his back. He was wearing a black suit and a coal black hat. Now the suspense was killing Pete. He had to see the stranger's face.

Pete just yelled out, "Thank you Mister, I thought I was a gonner for sure!"

Then, almost in slow motion (or so it seemed to Pete) the stranger turned and looked Pete in his eyes and said, "You're welcome, Partner!" And Pete saw that the man on the other end of the rope, his rescuer, was none other than Parson Fred!

Pete looked at Fred with amazement and exclaimed: "Fred, you spoke, it's a miracle!"

Fred said, "No, my speaking is no miracle, but hearing you, Texas Pete, pray, now that is a miracle! I didn't think I would ever hear such a thing! It was prettier than angel music to these old ears of mine. Now what did you mean when you told the Lord that you had 'just met Him'?"

Pete stood up straight and reached out to Fred

and took his hand and said, "Just a short time ago I trusted Jesus Christ as my personal Savior." Pete had never said it out loud before, and he was surprised how much he liked the sound of it!

A tear began to fall down the dry, dusty cheek of Parson Fred, and his voice began to quiver. He wanted to say something memorable and profound but all he could say through the tears was, "God is so good."

The warm handshake gave way to an enormous bear hug. But soon the moment of joy was clouded as Pete remembered the first time he met Fred. He remembered how he had humiliated the preacher when he first came to town, and Pete began to feel "funny." It was something he had only felt once before; he was "sorry!" He looked at Fred and Pete broke down in tears and said, "Can you ever forgive me for the way I treated you in the past?"

Fred could not hold back his emotions either. He looked Pete in his eyes and said, "Pete, from that day we first met, I have been praying for you. I guess I wrote every preacher within a hundred miles begging them to come here and talk to you, but only one fellow ever agreed to come. From what you told me a minute ago, I

bet you have already met him, his name is Parson Bill!"
Pete smiled and nodded. "Pete, I forgave you the day
you threatened me, but the beautiful thing is that now
God has forgiven you too!" The two men continued to
hug each other and then they broke out in the loudest
bunch of "hoopin and hollerin" that you have ever heard.
What a sight these two fellows must have been out there
on the plain waving their hats in the air and dancing a
happy jig!

After several minutes Fred finally asked, "So, why
were you traveling so quickly through Rattlesnake
Canyon?"

Pete suddenly remembered that he was on his
way to stop the *Chili Pepper Gang* from robbing the
stagecoach. As much as he was enjoying rejoicing with
Fred, he still had a job to do! Without a word, he whistled
for his trusty horse, Tobasco, and quicker than a wink,
Tobasco came running. He brushed off his hat, (which
never left his grasp during the whole rescue) and jumped
up on Tobasco and looked at Fred and said, "I was on my
way to stop the *Chili Pepper Gang* from robbing the stage
coach; do you want to come along?"

Fred smiled as he climbed on his horse and said,

"Lead the way." Pete yelled, "Giddyup," and with a snap of the reins they rode off as quickly as possible.

When they arrived at the stagecoach they noticed the *Chili Pepper Gang* already had it surrounded. That gang was so ornery, they had decided they were not going to wait for Pete! They were going to rob this coach without him. Pete's right hand man, Pepper Black, had been itching to take control of the gang for a long time, and he decided that this was his chance! There truly is no honor among thieves. There in front, riding in Pete's place, was Pepper Black. The gang was so sure that this was going to be an easy job that they only sent part of the gang. Beside Pepper Black, there was Lemon (pronounced Leemone) the Frenchman of the group; Pete's cousin, who's nickname was Yellow because he was afraid of everything; Sneezey, Pepper Black's sidekick, and the only woman to be part of the gang, the lovely Serrano Pepper. No one in the gang seemed to ever acknowledge that she was a girl, and she sure didn't act like one! The five of them had their guns drawn and the people in the coach had their hands up.

When Texas Pete showed up, Pepper Black looked at him with disgust and said, "It sure is about time you got here. We waited ten minutes on you! This coach is going to be a piece of cake!"

Pete, wasted no time and yelled to the whole gang, "Guys, you can't do this!"

Pepper Black looked around and asked "Why? Is the Sheriff coming or somethin?"

Pete had to think quick, no, the Sheriff was not coming, they had planned this job perfectly, but he had to say something. Before he could stop himself he blurted out, "Because God says it would be a sin to rob this stage coach!"

For about five seconds the gang members all looked at each other with puzzled looks on their faces, then the whole gang burst out into uncontrollable laughter. "Sin, he says...priceless," remarked Lemon. "Simply priceless." Pete thought for a moment that Yellow was going to fall off of his horse he was laughing so hard!

Pete stiffened his jaw and said "You can laugh all you want," as he turned Tobasco sideways to block Pepper from moving toward the stage, "But I am not gonna let you do this!"

When the gang realized he was not kidding, their laughter changed to anger. Pepper Black said, "Well if you'ns ain't for us, then you'ns agin us, and if I were you, I would leave before someone gits hurt." You could have heard a pin drop there in the Old West as Pepper Black and the gang drew down on Pete and Fred. The next sound heard was the hammers of five guns being pulled back. Pepper Black looked at Pete and asked, "Now, who you gonna be afraid of...me or God?"

Pete answered "I don't know all about this Bible stuff Pepper, but I know that this is sin, there is even a Commandment against it. I also know there is punishment for sin, and you guys need to be warned about what happens to sinners like you!"

Pepper Black was furious! "How dare you talk to us that way seeins' we have you outnumbered five to two!" With that he raised his pistol and aimed it right at Pete and said with disgust, "You had better say your prayers Mr. Religious Man."

The silence in the Prairie was broken by two things. The first thing they heard was the sound of a posse coming that way. While Pepper was trying to figure out what was going on he heard the second noise. Pepper was shocked to hear the sound of several shotguns being fired in the air. The people on the stage had taken advantage of the time Pete and Pepper had been talking to get out their shotguns and get ready to defend themselves! Pepper spun around. He and the gang could take these people on the coach, but now he had Pete behind him and, from the sound of the hooves pounding on the ground, there were at least 8 people riding up to protect the stage! Pepper realized that this was a fight he didn't want or need, so the *Chili Pepper Gang* holstered their guns, and Pepper Black turned to Texas Pete and said, "This had better be the last time you show your face around the *Chili Pepper Gang* or the next time WILL be your last." Pepper Black turned his horse with a tug of the reins, and with a commanding voice yelled, "Let's move out!" The *Chili Pepper Gang* seemed to easily follow their new self-appointed leader, and rode away quickly from the stagecoach.

Just then everyone on the coach broke out in a cheer of joy. Pete road up to the coach and calmly apologized for the gang's behavior. He then told them that he used to be the leader of the *Chili Pepper Gang* but that things were different now. All nine people on the coach listened as Pete told them his testimony, and then Parson Fred preached a short sermon to them. Pete had never heard Fred preach, but now he listened to every word. Fred told those on the coach that they were sinners and that Jesus loved them enough to die for them. It was sure a moving message. Pete watched as the stage driver broke down in tears, and passengers bowed their heads in the coach as Fred told them, "Whosoever shall call upon the name of the Lord shall be saved!" What a time it was as Pete and Fred knelt and prayed with each of them. Pete couldn't help but think that this was the start of something wonderful in Red Pepper, Texas.

After Pete had prayed with the last person, he looked up and there was Parson Bill. Pete wasn't sure, but he thought that the smile on Bill's face was the biggest one in history. Bill had gone to get the Sheriff and brought him to the coach. Bill had tried to rescue Pete, but now knew that God was taking care of him! Bill looked at Pete and asked, "What all happened here?"

Fred spoke up before Pete could say anything. "God took care of us Bill! And you should have heard Pete's testimony!" The three men rejoiced together as the Sheriff and his men led the coach into town.

After a few minutes of thanking the Lord for what He had done, Pete looked at his preacher friends and said, "Brothers, the *Chili Pepper Gang* needs the Lord. Will you pray with me that they will get saved?" The three men knelt together there on the plain and prayed like they had never prayed before. After all, if God could save Pete...He could save anybody.

Chapter 7

Friends of Fred

As the three men finished their little prayer meeting, Fred could see the concern that Pete had for his old friends. This was going to be a heavy burden for his new brother in Christ. Fred gave a quick glance and a wink to Parson Bill, and the two men nodded at each other. "What you need right now is some good old fashioned Red Pepper hospitality. I know you have lost all of your old friends, at least for now, so it is high time you got yourself some new friends!" The thought of new friends made Pete feel all warm inside. "Follow me," Fred continued, "And I will let you meet some of my dearest friends in the whole world. Everybody needs good friends, so I want to share my good old friends with my good new friend."

Parson Bill smiled and told Pete, "Since you are in good hands Pete, I am going to go into town and invite all those people from the coach to the Sunday services!" With that Parson Bill disappeared into a cloud of dust headed toward town, and Fred and Pete started heading to the western most outskirts of Red Pepper.

The two men rode for a while without talking, but Fred finally broke the silence. It was easy to see that he was uncomfortable with what he had to say. It is never easy to bring up bad memories. As the sky began to turn darker, there was a soft red glow as the setting sun began to sink further behind the mountains. The occasional howl of a coyote or the hoot of an owl were the only sounds on the plain as Fred began to speak. "Pete, I know you remember the first time we met." Pete couldn't say anything, he remembered well the day that he grabbed Parson Fred by the throat in front of the whole town and threatened and humiliated his friend. It was one of those memories, like so many others of his past, that he wanted to forget. He really respected Fred for being willing to bring it up, but part of him wanted to change the subject! "After you threw me to the ground in front of everyone, it seemed that the whole town was laughing at me! I just laid there with my eyes closed wishing it was all just a bad dream." Fred could see the sadness in Pete's eyes as he remembered the story. Truly, Pete was a different man now! Fred couldn't help but notice the tears of sadness on his cheek. He was glad that this Pete was his friend! Fred continued, trying to hurry so his friend would not have to suffer much more. "As I waited there on the ground in front of the saloon, the laughter began to fade and I could hear the footsteps as the crowd started breaking up. Soon, the laughter stopped, and I thought I was all alone. I slowly opened my eyes and noticed that there was still one couple standing over me. I held my breath and waited for them to point at me and laugh, but they didn't. They looked at me with love and compassion, and I knew these were good people!" Now the sun had almost completely set and the only light on Fred's face was from the beautiful stars in the sky, but Pete was amazed at the way Fred's face lit up as he continued his story. "The young man reached out his right hand and helped me up. Once he had me on my feet his grip tightened as he shook my hand and said 'Hi, my name is Hal Pepper and this is my wife Peno (pronounced Painyo) Pepper. Won't you come back to our place for a little while and rest and wash up?' That was the first of many trips to Hal and Peno Pepper's house for me. They were my only friends in town, and I have come to love them almost as much as my own family! When they found out about my desire to start a church here they gave me our very first church offering.

49

As a matter of fact they started putting money aside for Bibles, pews, and hymn books! Until Parson Bill got here, I often thought that their money was going to never be used, but now I know the Lord is going to raise up a church here in Red Pepper."

Pete had been focusing on every word as Fred told him the story. Now, as he looked ahead, he could see one of the cutest little farmhouses he had ever seen! It was a little white house with black shutters and this

beautiful hand made fence surrounding the front yard. As Fred dismounted and tied his horse to the fence, the night silence was broken by the cheery barking of a little black dog. Fred bent over and yelled "Scorcher! You come say hi to your old pal Fred!" Scorcher didn't slow down. He ran and jumped up into Fred's arms. It was a sight to see Fred grinning from ear to ear as Scorcher licked him all over his face.

Upon hearing Scorcher's barking, Hal and Peno Pepper came out on the porch and yelled, "Hey Fred come on in, and bring your friend with you!"

Fred leaned over to Pete and whispered, "If I know Peno at all, you are in for a real treat! I guarantee you that she has a pan of the most delicious homemade biscuits that you have ever tasted sitting there on the table for us!" Pete's mouth started to water, he had not eaten anything in hours!

When they arrived at the house, Fred grabbed Hal, and they gave each other a big hug. As Hal patted his friend on the back, the dust from the trail could be seen in the starry night. "My good friend, we sure have missed you. Come on in. Peno has just taken a pan of her famous homemade biscuits out of the oven, and has just opened a jar of her world famous strawberry preserves." In his excitement upon seeing his good friend he had not paid much attention to the stranger on the

51

porch. Pete's big hat, the dark night sky, and a whole day of prairie dust made Pete hard to recognize. Finally Hal asked Fred, "Who's your friend, Preacher?" Hal was in for the shock of his life when Texas Pete came out of the shadows and stood right in front of Hal. It had been a little over two years since he had seen that massive man. Their paths had not crossed since that day in front of the saloon. Hal's voice quivered as he looked at Pete, "Now, Mr. Pete, we sure don't want any trouble tonight." Pete was looking a little rough that night because he was tired, he had a lot on his mind, and he had not shaved nor showered in almost two days; and with all that, he looked even meaner than he had two years before.

As he was still trying to get over the shock of having the meanest outlaw in Texas on his front porch, he received an even bigger surprise as Fred looked at him and said, "Don't be afraid, Hal, this is not the same man you met two years ago!" The silent Preacher (as he had come to be known) spoke! Hal had never heard his voice! The day they met was the first day of Fred's silence.

Tears streamed down the face of Hal as he exclaimed, "Fred, you spoke!! I didn't think I would ever see the day!"

"Well get ready," answered Fred "There are a whole lot more surprises coming tonight!"

Even though Hal was afraid of Pete, he had the highest respect for Parson Fred, so, in spite of his reservations, he invited both men into the house. Hal and Fred walked in first, then Texas Pete made his way in, ducking his head so as not to bang it on the door frame. Hal watched as Pete took off his hat, and wiped his feet at the door; immediately Hal knew there was something different about Pete. Hal said, "Pete, come in and sit down; any friend of Fred's is a friend of mine." Texas Pete politely thanked him for the hospitality and sat down on the sofa (he took up two complete seats on the couch). As Pete sat on the couch with his hat in his hand, he heard what sounded like the voice of an angel coming from the kitchen. Peno, in her sweet soprano voice was singing... "Amazing Grace, how sweet the sound, that saved a wretch like me". Pete was shocked that there was a song that described what happened to him! He listened, hoping to hear the rest of the words, but Peno decided to just hum the rest. Just then Mrs. Pepper poked her head out of the kitchen. Pete couldn't

help but wonder how a voice as big as the one he was listening to could come out of a little tiny woman like that. She was a perfect match for her husband. Neither of them were very tall, and Pete couldn't help but think that they looked "cute" together. Peno yelled out from the doorway to the kitchen, "If I didn't know any better I'd think that Scorcher was excited to see Parson Fred."

Trying to play a joke on Peno, Fred said in a voice similar to Hal's, "He sure is." (she still did not know he could talk).

She grabbed a pan of biscuits and said as she walked into the living room, "You boys must be starv..." She stopped dead in her tracks as she found herself starring at none other than Texas Pete sitting on her sofa.

Noticing her discomfort, Pete smiled and said, "Excuse me Ma'am but if no one has prayed for those delicious smelling biscuits, I would be honored if you would let me, if it's O.K with your husband of course."

She tilted her head to the side to make sure she wasn't seeing...or hearing things and then replied in the sweetest little voice, "Well Mr. Pete, if you brought a prayer with you, I guess you can bless the food."

Pete stood up and held his hat up to his chest with both hands and prayed, "Lord, I want to thank you for saving me, thank you for the kind hospitality that I have already received from my brothers and sister in Christ, thank you for the food that has been prepared, but most importantly I pray for the entire *Chili Pepper Gang* that they will be saved, in Jesus' name; Amen." When Texas Pete opened his eyes and looked, there was not a dry eye in the house. No one would have thought Texas Pete would pray for anyone other than himself.

There was a long silence in the house for the next twenty seconds until Parson Fred added a hearty "Amen" to Pete's prayer. Peno was so shocked she almost dropped the pan of biscuits. Hal jumped up quickly to steady her hand and make sure she didn't faint. He just looked at the pale face of his wife and said matter-of-factly, "Oh, by the way honey, Parson Fred can talk now."

She just smiled and said, "Praise the Lord!" The four of them sat around the table and enjoyed each other's company and the delicious biscuits and preserves.

After a few minutes Pete looked at Peno and sheepishly asked "Maam, would it be too much trouble for you to teach me that song you were a singing in the kitchen? I don't believe I have ever heard anything so beautiful."

She smiled and nodded her head as she washed down the last bite of the last biscuit with a tall glass of spring water. "Come into the living room, Mr. Pete." There in the back corner of their quaint little living room was an old piano. Peno sat there and began to play and teach Pete the words to "Amazing Grace." Soon all four of them were standing around the piano and singing song after song. Pete was learning so much! But no matter how many wonderful songs he learned in his life he always wanted to go back to "Amazing Grace." The last verse was his favorite. Every time he sang it he got that "Rootin' and Tootin'" feeling again! When it was finally time for the evening to end, the Peppers invited them to stay in their guestroom, but Pete needed to head home. Parson Fred took them up on their offer. Pete untied Tobasco and started toward his house. There in the quiet night on the prairie, you could hear Pete's booming bass voice:

When we've been there ten thousand years
Bright shining as the sun
We've no less days to sing God's praise
Than when we first begun…

It sure was a lot more fun being a Christian!

This is the LAST chance you'll get from me." With a low voice he said, "One," getting a little louder, he said, "Two...THREE!"

Chapter 8

Finding the Gang

Pete woke up the next morning and started to heat some water on the stove. He was going to do something he hadn't done in days...take a bath! As Pete soaked in the hot bathtub, he remembered what fun last night had been and decided he was going back to Hal and Peno's house this morning. After he finished cleaning up, he got out his almost unused razor and shaved his face clean. He looked at himself

in the cracked mirror above his tiny sink and couldn't help but smile. He looked like a new person. He knew he was a new creature on the inside, but now he was starting to look like one on the outside too! He picked up his hat and dusted it off and headed out the door to the Peppers' house.

As he tied Tobasco up to the fence around Hal's front yard, Scorcher came running to him with his tail wagging. Most people who met the new Pete gave him

a double take, but not Scorcher. He decided he liked Texas Pete. Pete knelt down and the adorable little black dog just jumped into his arms and proceeded to lick every inch of Pete's face. Pete couldn't help himself and started to giggle! He couldn't remember the last time he had been this happy. "Get down off of Texas Pete now Scorcher!" Hal shouted from the porch.

As Pete put the dog down on the ground, he looked at Hal and grinned a sheepish grin. "I like your little dog, Hal."

Hal pointed to the furiously wagging tail of Scorcher and replied, "I think the feeling is mutual Pete!" And the two men headed inside.

As Pete stepped in he was immediately aware that the house smelled like coffee, biscuits, and bacon. He already knew Peno was a great cook, but he didn't know she cooked all the time! She poked her head out of the kitchen and ordered Pete to sit at the table with Fred; Pete didn't put up an argument. Hal joined them at the table and, as soon as Pete sat down, Peno put a plate in front of him. Pete never knew you could get that much breakfast on one plate. Pete grabbed his fork and was about to dig in when he heard Fred clear his throat...Pete had almost forgotten to pray! Parson Fred winked at him (Pete still had some learning to do) and prayed and thanked the Lord for the food. Pete was actually excited as he heard Fred pray for the *Chili Pepper Gang*. As soon as the prayer was over the three men dove into their breakfast. Every time they would finish a plate Peno would put a full one right in front of them. Pete became convinced that she enjoyed filling their plates as much as they enjoyed emptying them.

When the eating began to slow down Fred looked at Pete and said, "I'm glad you are here Pete. Hal, Peno, and I decided last night that we were gonna start a Saturday morning Bible study. Would you like to join us?"

Pete blurted out "You betcha!" Bible study, even the sound of it sounded great to Pete. He really didn't know much at all about the Bible, and it would be great to learn from his new friends.

They went into the living room, and Fred told them that they would begin with a time of sharing prayer requests. Hal said they should pray for Tom

Haught. Pete thought it was unusual to pray for a saloon owner at Bible study, but he didn't ask any questions. Peno requested prayer for a friend of hers that was supposed to be at church in the morning, and Parson Fred asked the group to pray for Bill and the message on Sunday. Now it was Pete's turn. Old Pete tried to hold back his emotions, but this was weighing heavier on his back than a hundred-pound bag of feed! Finally, when he could hold it in no longer, he began to cry as he said, "All my old friends are Commandment breakers and wicked sinners! According to Parson Bill, they are all headed to Hell without Jesus and somebody needs to warn them. I want to go right up to their hideout and tell them about Jesus! But yesterday at the stagecoach, Pepper Black told me that they would kill me if they ever saw me again, and I know he meant it when he said it. I just don't know what to do; will you guys pray for me?" It was easy for Fred, Hal, and Peno to see the burden that Pete was carrying for his old friends. The four of them got down on their knees and prayed for each other and their prayer requests.

After the prayer time was over, Fred decided to

start the Bible study with Bible accounts of God's protection.   Pete sat there with eyes as wide as saucers as he heard for the first time about God taking care of David when he went to fight the giant named Goliath. He soaked up the story of God's protection of Daniel in an entire den of lions. But the one that got his attention the most was when Fred told him about Shadrach, Meshach and Abednego and God's protection as they walked through a fiery furnace. Pete looked like a little boy in Sunday School as Fred told him about the "Fourth Man in the Fire" and that it was "Like the Son of God." Finally Pete jumped to his feet and yelled, "If God could protect them fellers, then He can sure enough protect me! Ya'll pray for me, I've got someplace important to go." And with that Pete walked out the door, jumped on Tobasco, and headed toward town.

Finding the gang would not be a problem. They spent every Saturday afternoon at the "hideout" planning the next week's robberies. The hideout was a run down old shack right behind the Haught and Spicey saloon. As he rode into town, he noticed that the streets were strangely quiet for a Saturday afternoon. Pete noticed a little old lady coming out of the bank, and he tipped his hat at her and grinned and offered her a cheery "Mornin Ma'am." Unfortunately she did not know there was a "new" Texas Pete so she ducked right back into the bank. Pete stopped his horse at the barbershop near the saloon and tied up Tobasco (he remembered that he had spent many days and nights in that saloon, but he knew now that he shouldn't even tie up his horse in front of the saloon! People might think he was in there).

As Pete headed toward the hideout, he glanced over and saw the old timer sitting on the porch of the saloon. Few people knew the old guy's name and even fewer people cared, but he was a part of the landscape of Red Pepper. For as long as Pete could remember, the same old guy had been sitting outside of the saloon with a spit pot next to him. When he saw Pete about to pass by he said, "We didn't see you in these here parts last night, Pete. The *Chili Pepper Gang* had an especially mean time here in town yesterday! They sure seemed to be mad at you...they kept saying something about a stage coach and a preacher. I don't know much Mr. Pete, but I am pretty sure that you are the last person that they want to see right now!"

Pete looked at the old man with such determination in his eyes that it made a shiver run up and down the old timer's back and said "Well they're gonna see me, and they're gonna listen to me, cause I'm gonna tell them about Jesus if it's the last thing I do!"

The old fellow looked at Pete and said, "Well, it was nice knowin' you Pete. I know you're a tough guy, but they have you outnumbered twenty-to-one!"

Pete just smiled and nodded, "But they don't know who's in the fire with me!" He nodded to the little old man and made his way to the front door of the hide out. Just before he knocked on the door with the secret knock, he paused for just a moment and prayed, "Lord, for the first time in my life, I am afraid of someone else. Please give me the courage you gave those people in the Bible! Amen."

Before he could even finish the secret knock the door swung open and there was Pepper Black. He looked at Pete and grinned a devilish grin and sneered, "Welcome to our hideout Mr. Religious Man!" Pepper pulled his gun from his holster and pointed it right at Pete. Pete had known Pepper Black a long time. He remembered the day that Pepper came to him and wanted to be a part of the *Chili Pepper Gang.* He knew from the beginning that Pepper was one of those rare people who was actually meaner than Pete! He was never afraid of anything and had no respect for anyone, especially the law. He was also a great planner when it came to robbing stagecoaches and banks. But for all of his meanness, fearlessness, and planning, there was one thing about Pepper that only Pete knew. it was the reason Pepper had never been the leader of the gang...Pepper couldn't hit the broad side of a barn! He could draw his gun as quickly as anyone in the Old West, but he was a horrible shot. This knowledge brought little comfort to Pete right now, because even Pepper couldn't miss from this close range. "I warned you didn't I? It is a good thing that you have started to believe in the Lord, because I am going to send you to meet Him! Now you have to the count of three to turn tail and run, and never come back. This is the LAST chance you'll get from me." With a low voice he said, "One," getting a little louder, he said, "Two...THREE!"

Chapter 9

Deliverance and Destruction

Just as Pepper Black yelled, "THREE," the door flew wide, and everyone was startled at the sound of a loud voice yelling, "NOOO!!"

The commotion took almost everybody by surprise. The gang all turned toward the door to see what was going on, and Pepper Black turned his head from Texas Pete's stare. Only Pete stayed focused. His eyes never left Pepper. The well-intentioned intruder's plan had backfired though. He had tried to stop Pepper from shooting at Pete, but his abrupt entrance had shocked the gang leader so much that he had fired a round...right at Pete! Slowly all eyes turned from the intruder at the door and everyone stared at Texas Pete. Now no one really knows what happened that day. Folks have offered lots of explanations, maybe the sound of the door swinging open startled Pepper, maybe it was just that he was such a horrible shot, many have even said that God Himself did a miracle that day. Whatever the reason, there stood Texas Pete with two bullet holes in his hat and not a scratch on him! Pepper's bullet had gone through the brim of Pete's ten-gallon hat, and right out the top of it, but it hadn't even touched ole Pete. They all watched with wonder as Pete took his hat off of his head and held it up to the light. Sure enough the bullet had gone straight through. Even Pepper Black was amazed.

Slowly the attention began to shift from Pete's hat to the intruder, still standing at the door. They were all shocked as they recognized the old man from the porch of the saloon. He was standing there with his shotgun at his side and he, too, was just staring at Texas Pete's "holy" hat (as it came to be known). He had burst through the door ready to protect Pete, but now he wasn't so sure Pete needed protection. Staring at the hat, he realized who was in the fire with Pete that day. Quickly he stiffened his jaw and brought his shotgun back up and informed the gang, "Anybody tries any funny stuff, and I'll fill your hides with buck shot!" With that warning the whole gang lifted their hands in the air with one exception. Pepper Black held his gun out in front of his face and stared at it. Then a look of sheer fear came over his face and he dropped it to the ground, turned tail, and ran out the door. The old timer yelled at him as he ran, "You better run you ornery varmint!"

The gang's attention shifted to the doorway of the hideout. There stood Texas Pete in the entry way. He was so large that he blocked most of the door, but there was a little light coming through from behind him. It was as if his whole body was framed in a soft glow. The gang noticed that he was clean-shaven, and his clothes looked clean. As they continued to stare at their former leader they also saw that he wasn't even wearing a holster. They were further amazed when they noticed what was in his hand. Many times they had watched Pete draw his gun, and they were expecting that his trusted six shooter would be in his hand. To their surprise Pete was clutching his brand new Bible! Even when he was coming to face down the worst gang in Texas, Pete knew he needed the Lord and his Bible more than any gun.

It began to dawn on the gang that even without Pepper, they still had Pete outnumbered nineteen to one. Lemon looked at Pete and asked, "Pete, have you gone plumb loco that you would come in here to face us and not even bring a gun to defend yourself? Do you really think you can take all of us with just a Bible?"

Pete smiled and said, "No, Lemon, but I know two things, one, I am no match for all of you, and two, you are no match for the Lord!" With that Pete lifted his new Bible over his head and pointed to the Heavens.

Lemon smirked and said, "What makes you so sure that the Lord is going to protect you against us?"

Pete didn't even pause to think, but he gave Lemon the first answer that came to his mind. "If the Lord can protect a shepherd against a giant, and keep a man safe in a den of lions, and protect three Hebrew boys in a fiery furnace, and answer an old cowboy's prayer and deliver him out of a rattlesnake pit, then I believe He is going to protect me from you guys!"

Sneezy spoke up, "Pete, you may believe all that Bible stuff, but I want to see some proof! What makes you so sure that your God can protect you from a six shooter?" Pete didn't say a word, he just slowly reached his arms to the top of his head and took off his trusty ten-gallon hat and held it up to the doorway of the hideout. The afternoon sunlight shined right through the two holes left by the bullet that Pepper Black fired just a few minutes before. The room went deathly quiet as each member of the gang stepped forward and put their index finger through the holes in Pete's hat.

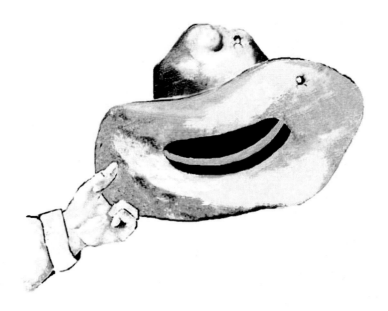

Finally, Yellow broke the silence. "Pete, I sure would like to know more about your God. I think I'd like to have Him as my God too!" There were lots of nods from the rest of the gang as each agreed with Yellow.

Pete told the boys, "I don't have all the answers fellas, but I can tell you what Parson Bill told me." Pete then began to tell the gang that they were all sinners. He told them that Romans 3:23 says that "All have sinned and come short of the glory of God." The guys sure weren't going to disagree. If there was ever a group of people that knew they were sinners it was the *Chili Pepper Gang*. Then Pete began to tell them that there was punishment for being a sinner.

Serrano asked, "Does God send you to prison like the Sheriff?"

"No," Pete said, "The Bible says 'For the wages of sin is death'!" The guys looked at Pete with sheer terror on their faces as Pete explained that "death" was talking about a horrible place of punishment called "Hell"!

At that point the old timer from the front of the saloon blurted out, "How do a bunch of sinners like us stay out of a place like that, Pete?" With a kind, knowing smile on his face, Pete began to tell them about Jesus. He told them that Jesus loved everyone of them even though they were wicked. You could have heard a pin drop as Pete told them about Jesus dying on the cross. Lemon actually started to cry when Pete told the gang how much the Lord had suffered that day and that He had done it all for them. Pete explained to them that "The gift of God is eternal life, through Jesus Christ our Lord."

That was when Serrano spoke up and said "Gift! Gift!!! You mean this whole thing is FREE?!?!"

Pete smiled and said "Yes Serrano, we can't earn something this wonderful, and we sure can't steal it, but God will give it to us!" He told them that the Bible says, "Whosoever shall call upon the name of the Lord shall be saved." Then Pete looked around the room and asked, "Would anyone here like to receive God's gift of Salvation today?" It was startling that the first hand that went up was Yellow's. He was always afraid of everything, but he wasn't afraid today. Soon hands were going up all over the room. Then Pete started going to each one of them, and had the privilege of praying with all nineteen of them one at a time. He was able to hear each member of the gang pray, in child-like faith and receive Jesus as personal Savior. Pete couldn't stop crying as he thanked the Lord for answering his prayer about his friends.

When all had finished praying and stood up, every member of the *Chili Pepper Gang* was smiling through the tears of repentance. Lemon finally spoke up and asked, "Does this mean we are 'saved'?"

Pete looked at him and said, "It sure does Lemon."

Then Yellow asked "What about Pepper? He didn't get saved." Pete didn't think that anything could have made him sad at this moment, but the thought of Pepper Black still needing to get saved was still a burden on his heart. Pete just said, "We need to keep praying for Pepper. God can still save him.

While the *Chili Pepper Gang* was rejoicing about getting saved, Pepper Black was riding furiously through the plain. His mind was racing as his horse galloped through the dusty desert outside of Red Pepper. He couldn't believe that Pete's God protected him, but he also couldn't believe he was THAT bad a shot. He had known nothing but crime his whole life, and no "Religious Man" was going to change him. The problem was, that Pepper had never respected anyone, until he met Pete. Pete was the first "Real" man he had ever met. He was rough and tough and fearless, and now he was one of those "Christians!" Pepper was determined to forget about Pete and the gang and start his own group of ruffians to terrorize the West.

As his horse's hooves pounded on the ground, Pepper was completely distracted by the thoughts that were flooding his mind. He didn't see the cliff coming up. His trusty horse was speeding toward the edge of Banana Pepper Canyon. Less than fifty feet from the drop off, the horse came to a screeching stop and sent

Pepper flying over the mighty stallion's head, hurtling toward the edge of the cliff. Pepper tried to stop as he hit the ground. He reached for anything he could grab but couldn't stop his momentum. Then he let out a yell, and as quick as a wink Pepper Black went over the edge of Banana Pepper Canyon. The last thought that went through his mind as he went over the cliff was that he wished he had stayed with the gang and listened to Pete!

Yes, there was starting to be a new "Legend of Texas Pete."

Chapter 10

Pete and the Gang Ride Again

Pete and the boys were still rejoicing back at the hideout. Hugs were being shared, and tears of joy were flowing. After a little while Pete started telling the guys about Hal and Peno. The gang was excited about meeting more Christians (and they were also excited about those homemade biscuits and strawberry preserves). Pete got everyone's attention and said "Come on guys, I'll introduce them to you." The gang all walked together to the barbershop to get Tobasco. As Pete reached his trusty horse, he noticed there was something stuck to the saddle. He unfolded the piece of paper and realized it was a flier from Parson Bill. He read it out loud to the gang.

Everyone is invited to the first meeting of the Red Pepper Baptist Church.

Place: *The Big Red Barn on the Outskirts of Town*

When: *March 5, 1849 at 11:00 AM*

What to Expect: *Singing, Preaching, and Dinner on the ground!*

Everyone is invited
to the first meeting of the
Red Pepper Baptist Church
Place: The Big Red Barn
on the outskirts of town
When: March 5, 1849, 11AM

What to expect: Singing,
Preaching, Dinner
on the ground!

Parson Bill had been putting up those fliers for two days; Sneezy looked at Pete and said, "Great grandmother's apple pie, that is tomorrow!"

Pete yelled "Come on boys, we have some ridin' to do!" They all jumped on their horses and rode like the wind all the way to Hal and Peno's house. As Pete got off his horse Scorcher came running. Boy did that little dog love Texas Pete. As a matter of fact Scorcher loved all the guys except Lemon! Pete pounded on the door of the adorable home of Hal and Peno. When Hal came to the door Pete smiled and motioned toward the gang and said, "I brought you some new friends!" As Hal scanned the rough faces of the *Chili Pepper Gang,* he could see that these weren't the same criminals that had been terrorizing the town. They were changed. Hal couldn't quite put his finger on it. Maybe it was their smiling faces, or the polite way they stood to one side as he opened the door, or maybe it was the yellow fliers they were holding in their hands; whatever it was Hal sure did like it. Hal slapped his hand on his thigh and gave out a big "YeeHah! God sure does answer prayer doesn't he Pete?!"

Pete smiled and said, "He sure does, Hal, but there will be plenty of time for rejoicing later. We've got some work to do." As Pete said this he handed the flier to Hal.

"We sure do," Hal replied. "We need to start gathering up some Bibles and hymn books! I know where we can buy 'em, but I can't get them all on my horse."

Pete hit Hal on the back so hard he lost his breath and said, "You're not alone on this one Hal, me and the gang are here to help. I figure if we each carried five song books and five Bibles that would give us almost one hundred of each for the service tomorrow." Hal told Pete where to go to get the Bibles and then where to get the song books, and the boys headed out! What a sight it was to see the gang headed out of town on a mission for the Lord.

One funny thing happened as they went. About a mile out of town Yellow saw a stagecoach headed the opposite way, back into town. He motioned for the boys and the whole gang stopped and lined the road to town. When the coach pulled up to the Chili Pepper roadblock the driver threw up his hands and threw down his shotgun. From the back of the coach two men threw out the strongbox with the railroad payroll in it!

What a sight it was when Yellow and Pete rode up beside the stage and handed the driver and the passengers their fliers for the church service. "You mean you fellers don't mean to rob us?" Asked the coach driver.

"No way," said Yellow, "We're not that kind of gang anymore! But we did want to invite you all to go to church with us tomorrow!" All of a sudden the passengers in the coach began to cheer for Texas Pete and the boys. Pete suggested that Yellow and a couple of other gang members should escort the stage to town. The rest of them would carry a couple extra Bibles in their saddlebags and that way the coach would be sure to be safe. Word spread all over Texas as fast as a brush fire as people began to talk about Pete and the gang stopping a stage to invite people to church. Yes, there was starting to be a new "Legend of Texas Pete."

Chapter 11

Who Is Coming to Church?

Parson Bill did not know what to expect that Sunday morning. He knew Fred, Hal, and Peno would be there, and there were two people from the Coach he and Pete had rescued who had promised to come. But he just didn't know how many town folk from Red Pepper would be at the first service. He was hoping Pete would be there, but even if he wasn't, six would be a good first attendance. At 10:45 Bill was happy to see Fred and Peno walk in. He wondered where Hal was but didn't want to ask right away. He didn't want to embarrass Peno. The three of them sat there in an awkward silence staring at each other. Fred and Peno had a great secret, but they wanted it to be a surprise for the Preacher. See, Bill didn't know what all had happened with Pete and the gang, and he had no way of knowing what was going to happen next.

About 10:50 four people, including the driver from the stage that Pete rescued from Pepper Black, came walking through the door. Bill had prayed that two would come, and the Lord had doubled his prayer!

Then in came an old man that Bill thought he had never met. The old fellow was clean-shaven and had on a beautiful almost new black suit. The man walked straight up to Bill and said, "Morning Reverend!" and sat down in the front row. It wasn't until the old fellow leaned his chair back that Bill realized it was the old guy from in front of the old saloon!! It was the first time that Bill had seen him without tobacco in his mouth. Bill didn't know that right after the old fellow got saved that he spit out his tobacco for the last time!

The crowd continued to file in. Next, four families walked in, each carrying one of Bill's invitation flyers. With husbands, wives and children, that was sixteen more. There were already twenty-four people there! Bill was sure that Hal would get there, and he had his surprise guest coming, so that meant they would have at least twenty-six. What a blessing! And it was still only 10:52. They might even get another person or two, and of course, Bill was still praying in his heart the Pete would be there.

Then Bill heard a great commotion outside and started toward the door. It sounded like a crowd was forming in the alley behind the church. This was Bill's only fear on this day and the only thing that could have dampened his spirits. That mean old *Chili Pepper Gang* was going to try to stop the service. Then Bill's worst fears were realized as the door swung open and there stood Yellow and Lemon! Bill struggled to find the right words to say to avoid the confrontation that was coming, but before he could speak Yellow broke the silence. "Where do you want these hymn books and Bibles preacher?" he said as he politely removed his hat from his head. At that moment Bill had no idea what to say. He had stood in front of crowds before, had preached many sermons, and God had always given him the exact words to say. But as he stared at Pete, Hal, and nineteen members of the *Chili Pepper Gang*, all dressed up, all clean shaven, and all carrying five Bibles and five song books, for the first time in his life, he was speechless! All he could think was, "God is SOOO Good!" But there was no way to make the words come out of his mouth.

Instead, Fred spoke up and said, "Fellows, why don't you give one Bible and one song book to everyone here, keep one of each for yourselves, and put the rest on the empty chairs." The boys all smiled and gave Parson Fred a nod that silently said, "yessir." With that the gang all found their seats. It was funny to watch as they all tried to sit on the front row next to Pete.

Just before 11:00 five people walked in that Bill had never met before. He greeted them at the back door and introduced himself to them as the preacher. Each person gave the Parson their name and added that they had just arrived into town on yesterday's stage. As they walked further into the building, Bill watched each of them walk up and hug Pete and Yellow. Now this was something that you didn't see every day!

Right as Bill got up to start the service, the back door opened one more time and the congregation turned to see the last two first timers. The first person they saw was the beautiful Belle Pepper. She was the quiet school teacher from town. She seldom talked to anyone except her students. Some folks thought she was shy, but the real truth was that she was embarrassed. With a last name like "Pepper" and a brother like Yellow, she never felt right about showing her face in public. It was nice to see her in her beautiful dress, carrying an ornate parasol and wearing the prettiest hat.

Everyone smiled at her as she came in, but the biggest smile belonged to Texas Pete. As Belle scanned the crowd looking for a seat, Pete elbowed Yellow to move him out of the seat next to him. The first elbow was subtle, but the second wasn't. As Yellow rubbed his shoulder and grimaced in obvious pain, he got up and left the seat next to Pete empty. Belle walked slowly to the front and timidly sat down in the empty seat. She couldn't take her eyes off of Pete. She kept telling herself that it was because he looked so different, but she was pretty sure it was because he was so handsome! The other person that came in with Belle just slipped quietly down into a seat on the back row. His face had been hidden from view by Belle's beautiful parasol and, since every one was staring at Belle, no one gave him a second look.

With the forgotten stranger in the back there were now fifty-two people at the first service. Bill had never been this excited!

Chapter 12

The First Service

Parson Bill stood behind the pulpit and said: "Welcome everyone to the first service of Red Pepper Baptist Church! Let's all stand and sing my favorite hymn, number 62 in your books... 'Amazing Grace'!" With that everyone stood and started singing. Most of the *Chili Pepper Gang* tried to follow but they just didn't know the words. Texas Pete, however, had been singing this song ever since that first night at Hal and Peno's house. The building almost rattled with his deep baritone voice resonating as he sang to the top of his lungs. Beside him, in a voice as sweet as an angel's, came the soprano sound of Belle Pepper singing along. Pete could not help but think that they made a wonderful duet together, if he did say so himself! By the time they reached that last verse, Pete's favorite, the entire congregation had stopped singing and were all listening to Pete and Belle. Tears were running down Pete's face, and he was getting that "Rootin', Tootin' feeling again. But Pete wasn't alone. There were sniffles and shouts of "Amen!" from all over the congregation. Yellow was trying to hide the tears that were coming down his cheek, as were all the gang members. Never, had they heard a song being sung with that kind of joy. Years later, as the new Legend of Texas Pete began to grow, people would say that you could hear Texas Pete singing from one end of town to the other. Although that was probably an exaggeration, there is no question that everyone in the room heard it! What a start to the first service.

Then Parson Bill walked to the pulpit and had everyone turn in their Bibles to II Corinthians chapter five and verse seventeen. "Therefore if any man be in Christ he is a new creature..." Bill's voice was strong as he read. "In the last few days our town has witnessed many miracles. We have seen people get saved that the world thought would never believe, and although each testimony would be a blessing, I would like to share one particular story with you this morning." As he spoke, every one was sure he was going to tell about Texas Pete's salvation. Parson Bill began by describing a fearsome gangster, that broke every law, intimidated every Sheriff, mocked every preacher, and rejected every witness. People were sure now that he

was talking about Pete. The Preacher continued with
the story of how that outlaw found himself hanging by a

thread and his time was running out. How this terrible man finally called out and asked for the Lord's help. This had to be the story of Texas Pete, the people thought. But then the Preacher told them that the man, as he hung over the ledge between death and life, had cried out to the Lord and said, "God, if you give me one more chance, I promise I will listen!" No sooner had he finished those words when a hand reached over the ledge and pulled up the hopeless man! With that Bill told the congregation what he had told the mystery man as they sat staring over the ledge into the deep canyon below. The preacher had told him that he was a sinner and that the Bible taught that "The wages of sin is death." The hardened outlaw had listened as the preacher told him about the love that God had shown by sending His Son, Jesus, to die on a cross. The criminal could not believe that someone as wonderful as Jesus could love someone as bad as he was, but the preacher assured him that "God so loved the world!" As Parson Bill continued the story, the people kept trying to figure out who he was talking about, this was not the story of Texas Pete getting saved. Each person sat up a little straighter, and listened a little more intently as Bill continued. "I told him there on the canyon side that 'Whosoever shall call upon the name of the Lord, shall be saved' and there, just a few feet from where he almost died, the gangster received Christ as his Savior and became a new creature! I would like to introduce him to you!" With that Parson Bill pointed to the back of the room and there, standing...and smiling was Pepper Black! As Pete turned around and saw him, he let out a loud "YeeHah!" He was pretty sure there was a more appropriate thing to say in church but that was all he could think of!

With that, Parson Bill had everyone bow their heads and close their eyes. He asked the crowd that day if anyone there needed to be a New Creature. He was thrilled to see four hands go up! As they came out of their seats to the front, Hal, Peno, Fred, and Pete each took one person out and talked to them. What a joy it was to share with the rest of the brand new church that four people had gotten saved that day! This had truly been the best "first service" in the history of Texas churches!

After they sang "Victory in Jesus", Parson Fred came up front to close the service in prayer. As Fred finished with "Amen" Parson Bill spoke up and said, "And all God's people said?" And with that the church responded with forty-nine "Amens" and three more "YeeHaws!"

Pete reached down to pick up his Bible from the seat and saw Belle's Bible sitting there. He picked it up and nervously said, "Miss Belle, I would be honored if you would allow me to carry your Bible, and walk you to your house. There may be an outlaw out there!"

With that she smiled and said "Mister Pete, I don't think there are any more outlaws in Red Pepper, Texas; but I would be honored if you would walk me to my door." It was from that moment on, he and Belle were inseparable. It is uncertain how it all came to pass, but it was only a few months later that another set of fliers was being passed out all over town inviting everyone to the wedding ceremony of Texas Pete and Belle Pepper. Some matches are made in Heaven, theirs was made in church!

Chapter 13

The Telegram

Things in Red Pepper, Texas had certainly changed since Texas Pete and the *Chili Pepper Gang* changed their ways. People were able to walk down the street day or night without fear, the bank had not been robbed in nearly two years, and Haught and Spicey's saloon had shut down and become a dry goods store. The cursing and swearing that used to be heard from the streets had now turned to polite and friendly conversations about the wonderful church services they were having at Red Pepper Baptist Church. The sound of gunfighters calling out other gunfighters in the city square had been changed to the sound of cowboys humming, whistling, and even singing "Amazing Grace"! Yes this town truly changed when Christ was invited into the lives of the people.

Things had changed at the church too. Parson Bill had asked Parson Fred to be his Assistant Pastor, and Pepper Black was teaching the teen Sunday School class. Each Sunday you could hear Serrano and Lemon in the choir, and Yellow was studying to be a circuit riding preacher! The church had grown quite large for a prairie church. Every Sunday more than two hundred and fifty people crowded into the beautiful white building with the tall steeple that they had built on the land that Tom Haught had donated to the church. Lives had been changed, a church had been planted, and a town had been saved! Texas Pete was now a model citizen and a faithful member of his local church. Stories of his zeal for serving the Lord and his fearlessness when sharing the Gospel were spreading all over Texas, New Mexico and Arizona. A rumor had even been spread that Pete was going to be the first deacon at the church. Yes, Pete and Belle were as happy and content as two termites in a lumber yard. They had planned to start a family, build a house, and stay in Red Pepper, Texas for the rest of their lives. But God had a different plan for Pete and Belle.

On Wednesday, March 19, 1851 while Texas Pete and Parson Fred were preparing for the mid week Bible study, there was an urgent knock on the door of the church house. Pete hurried to the door and opened it. There in front of him stood a little fellow with thick glasses, a white shirt, and an armband above his elbow. "May I help you friend?" asked Pete.

The man answered and said, "I have a telegram for you, Mr. Texas Pete." Now Pete had never received a telegram nor did he know what to do with one. Texas Pete looked worried and asked what a telegram was. The short nervous man answered impatiently, "It is an urgent letter from someplace far away, and I believe you are supposed to read it!" The man handed Pete the telegram and turned with a huff and walked away. Pete just stood there, shocked, as he read the telegram out loud:

Texas Pete had not seen Pepper Jack in years. How well he could remember those old days of robbing and breaking laws. He and Pepper rode rough shod

over the entire northern part of Texas. "Pete and Pep"
everyone called them. Pete had thought they would be
plundering together their entire lives. Then, old Pepper
Jack "got religion"! He went to visit his sick brother in
the hospital outside of Dallas. Pete had often thought
that Pepper Jack's brother, Monterey, was a little
weird. He was always talking about church and other
religious "nut" kinda things. Anyway, after three or four
days at the hospital with Monterey, Pepper was a
completely different person.   Pepper had tried to
explain what happened to him, but Pete didn't want to
hear it. Pete called Pepper a "low down dirty coward"
and walked away. Now that Pete looked back on it, he
knew exactly what had happened to Pepper! He sure
was excited to hear from him again, but it sounded like
his friend was in some serious trouble.

Pete finished reading the telegram, and looked
at Fred with a confused look on his face. "Fred," Pete
began carefully, "I don't know what to do. A big part of
me wants to stay here in Red Pepper with you, Bill, Hal,
Peno, and the gang. I love our quiet little town and our
wonderful church, and I can't imagine leaving. But
another part of me knows that my old friend Pepper is

in trouble and needs my help. What do you think I should do?"

Fred smiled and said, "I'd love to give you an answer Pete, but I can't. I think you oughtta talk to Parson Bill and Belle, but most importantly I think you should pray about it. You should never make a decision without praying about it first. I don't have the answer you need, neither does Bill or even Belle; but God sure does!"

Pete began praying right then, and his friend Fred joined him. It was funny because, almost as soon as he started praying, Pete felt like he knew for sure what God wanted. He thanked Fred for the prayers and ran outside and jumped on Tobasco and headed home to see Belle. He told her of his long history with Pepper Jack and how he felt the Lord leading. She smiled and told Pete that she was willing to follow him as he followed the Lord. Then she and Pete knelt there in the living room and prayed. Pete loved it so much when they prayed together. After they prayed, Belle asked Pete, "How are you going to tell Parson Bill that we are leaving?" Pete didn't know, but he sure was nervous. This kind of news could kill a preacher!

Pete spent the next two hours rehearsing what he would say to Bill. He quietly prayed that the news would not hurt him or the church. About thirty minutes before the service was to start, Pete saw Parson Bill riding up to the church. Pete ran out to meet his friend, his pastor, and his Bible teacher. Without a word, Pete handed the telegram to Bill. It seemed to Pete like it took the Parson two hours to read the short message. Finally, Bill's eyes met Pete's, and the preacher said, "So, when are you leaving?"

Pete couldn't believe his ears. "You think I should go Preacher?"

Without hesitation Bill said, "Of course Pete, your friend needs help starting a church, and defeating a gang. I can't think of anyone with more experience in those two areas than you!"

Pete laughed a hearty baritone laugh, "You know preacher, you're right, as usual. No wonder God wants us to go!"

At the end of the service Texas Pete and his wife came to the front; Parson Bill told the church about their decision. The auditorium was filled with mixed emotions, everyone was happy that Pete and Belle were following God's will, but they were all sad that they were losing them! Parson Bill asked Pete and Belle if they would like to share a brief testimony. Pete was so shook up that all he could say was "We sure do love you all and we are going to miss you! If you are ever in Cheddarville please stop in." With that, he wiped his eyes with his hankie and sat down. Now it was Belle's turn. Pete noticed that she seemed so calm and collected. As she looked out on the congregation she simply said, "I agree with Pete, we are going to miss you all. We are excited about this new chapter in our lives, but we need your prayers as we go. Will you please pray for Pete, and me...and ...the...baby!"

Belle said nothing else and just sat down beside Pete. That old cowboy lifted his face out of his hankie and whispered to himself "baby." He looked at Belle and said a little louder, "Baby" then his face broke into a smile and he said, "Did you say, BABY?" Belle just nodded her head. Now Pete had been saved for over two years and had been in many church services. He knew what was appropriate to say in church and what wasn't; but he could not help himself. He jumped to his feet and yelled to the top of his lungs, "YEEEEEHAAAAW! I'm gonna be a daddy!"

After the service each member came by and hugged Pete and Belle and promised they would pray for them. Tom Haught, Yellow, and Parson Fred all three promised to visit Pete in Cheddarville. After the handshaking, crying, and hugging were over, Hal asked Pete to step outside. He walked over to the back of his wagon and pulled out a little pile of black fur and handed it to Pete. "What's this?" Pete asked as the little pile of fur started licking his face.

"This is Scorcher's first puppy, Fireball." We know how you've always loved Scorcher, and wanted a dog just like her, and here he is!" Pete couldn't stop grinning. A baby, a puppy, and a new adventure for Texas Pete all in the same day!

The next day Pete and Belle loaded up their wagon and headed out of town. As they reached the town limits they were surprised to see the whole town there to say goodbye. The new Mayor (The old timer from outside the saloon) shook his hand and said, "You will never know what you mean to this town! In your honor we are changing the name of Mount Cayenne to Texas Pete Mountain!" Pete thanked him and flipped the reins, and they left Red Pepper Texas behind them. They would miss it so, but they would always cherish the memories.

"I think you are going to be a good daddy, Mr. Texas Pete!" Belle stated as they headed North.

Pete smiled and said, "What are we gonna name our little tyke? How 'bout Pete Jr?"

Belle just smiled and said, "I was thinking 'Cilantro' for a girl and 'Picante' for a boy?"

Texas Pete put his arm around his wife and said, "I love it Little Miss Pepper!"